For my husband, Silvio, who gives life;

for Barbara, who nurtures the small and precious things;

and for my brother, Liam, who has seen it all and is always there

Light, Bright Light

Published 2021

Library of Congress Control Number: 2020920706

ISBN 978-1-7347857-4-6 (paperback)
ISBN 978-1-7347857-5-3 (ebook)

Conor Detwiler
Scituate, MA
www.conordetwiler.com
inquiry@conordetwiler.com

LIGHT, BRIGHT LIGHT
CONOR DETWILER

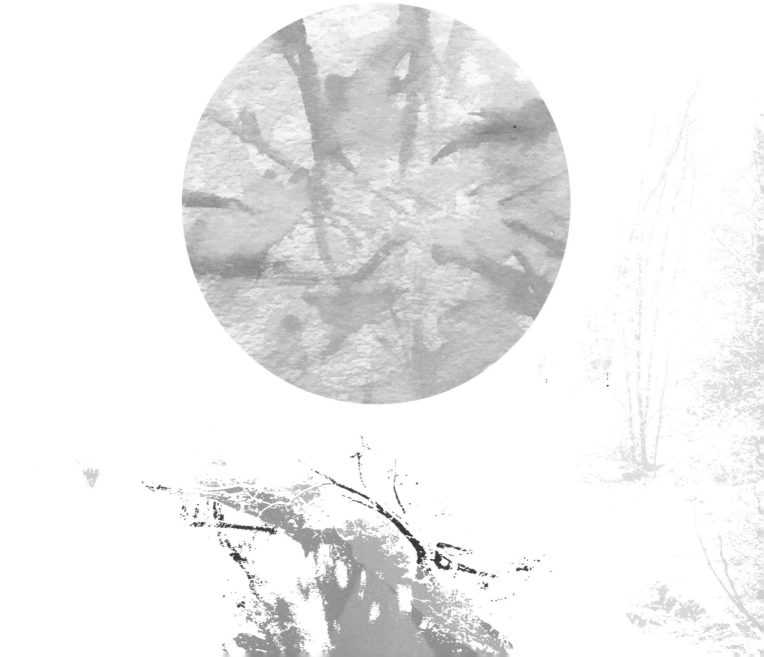

Sometimes there are
so many

birds in your head

that you feel confused. But

it's not forever. Behind the noisy, flapping thoughts

the sky is open and free.

Breathe in.
Can you feel the life
in your body?

You are light.

Sometimes
your feelings

are so cloudy

and sad.

But

it's not forever.
Tears come like warm rain

to wash over the land.

Breathe in.
Can you feel the air move your belly?

You are light.

Sometimes
your body

feels so

prickly

and angry.

But

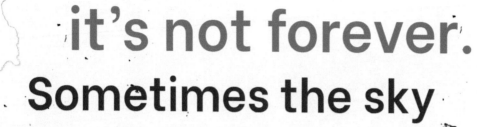

it's not forever.
Sometimes the sky

needs to storm.

Breathe in.
Can you feel your feet
on the ground?

You are light.

Sometimes
there is
so much
fear

that
you
can't
move.   But

it's not forever.
All those scary feelings

just swirl away like smoke.

Breathe in
and **breathe out.**
Hwwwwwwwwww!

You are light.

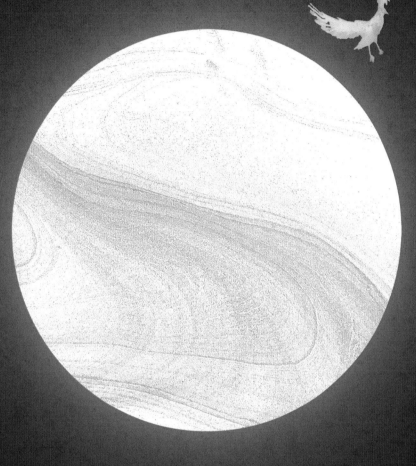

Sometimes
there is
so much
to do

and you can't sit still. But

it's not forever.
Feel the glitter of movement

come and go.

Breathe in.
Can you feel the quiet
in your heart?

You are light.

As you listen to
feelings come

and

then take flight,

can you feel that

you are light?